This book belongs to:

....

Illustrated by Véronique Petit.

Copyright © 2017

make believe ideas ltd

The Wilderness, Berkhamsted, Hertfordshire, HP4 2AZ, UK.

www.makebelieveideas.com

Nursery Rhymes

make
believe
ideas

HUMPTY DUMPTY

Humpty Dumpty sat on a wall.
Humpty Dumpty had a great fall.
All the king's horses and all the king's men
couldn't put Humpty together again.

Five little speckled frogs

Five little speckled frogs
sat on a speckled log,
eating some most delicious bugs,
yum, yum!
One jumped into the pool,
where it was nice and cool.
Then there were four green speckled frogs,
glug, glug!

HEY diddle diddle

Hey diddle diddle,
the cat and the fiddle,
the cow jumped over the moon.
The little dog laughed
to see such fun,
and the dish ran away with the spoon.

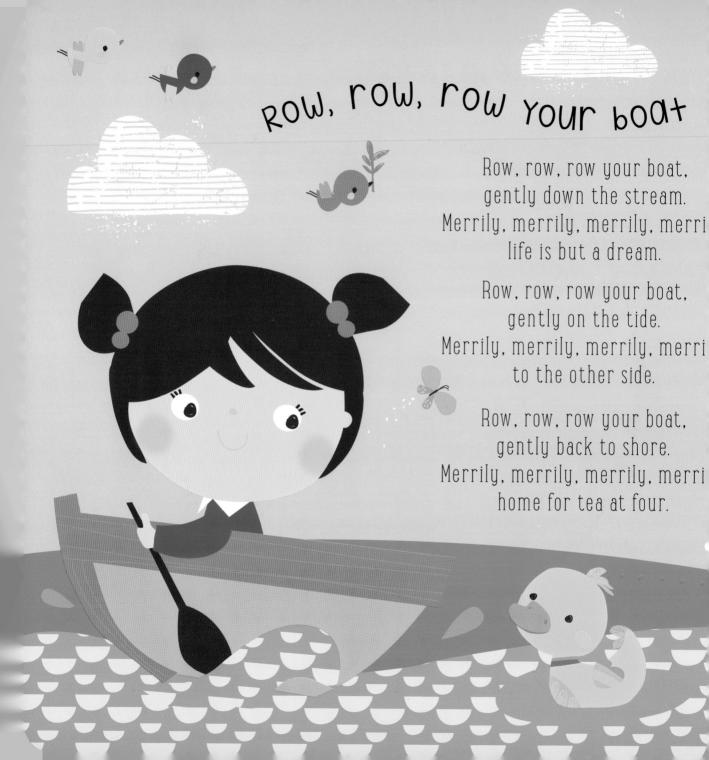

Row, row, row your boat

Row, row, row your boat,
gently down the stream.
Merrily, merrily, merrily, merri
life is but a dream.

Row, row, row your boat,
gently on the tide.
Merrily, merrily, merrily, merri
to the other side.

Row, row, row your boat,
gently back to shore.
Merrily, merrily, merrily, merri
home for tea at four.

Baa, baa, black sheep

Baa, baa, black sheep,
have you any wool?
Yes sir, yes sir,
three bags full.
One for the master,
one for the dame,
one for the little boy
who lives down the lane.

Hickory dickory dock

Hickory dickory dock,
the mouse ran up the clock.
The clock struck one,
the mouse ran down.
Hickory dickory dock!

Here we go round the mulberry bush

Here we go round the mulberry bush,
the mulberry bush,
the mulberry bush.
Here we go round the mulberry bush
on a cold and frosty morning.

This is the way we clap our hands,
clap our hands,
clap our hands.
This is the way we clap our hands
on a cold and frosty morning.

Twinkle, twinkle, little star

Twinkle, twinkle, little star,
how I wonder what you are.
Up above the world so high,
like a diamond in the sky.
Twinkle, twinkle, little star,
how I wonder what you are.

Mary, Mary, quite contrary

Mary, Mary, quite contrary,
how does your garden grow?
With silver bells and cockleshells
and pretty maids all in a row.

Pat-a-cake

Pat-a-cake, pat-a-cake, baker's man,
bake me a cake as fast as you can.
Pat it and prick it and mark it with
and put it in the oven for Baby and m

Jack and Jill

Jack and Jill went up the hill
to fetch a pail of water.
Jack fell down and broke his crown,
and Jill came tumbling after.

Up Jack got and home did trot
as fast as he could caper;
and went to bed to mend his head
with vinegar and brown paper.

The Wheels on the Bus

The wheels on the bus go round and round,
round and round, round and round.
The wheels on the bus go round and round, all day long.

The wipers on the bus go swish, swish, swish;
swish, swish, swish; swish, swish, swish.
The wipers on the bus go swish, swish, swish, all day long.

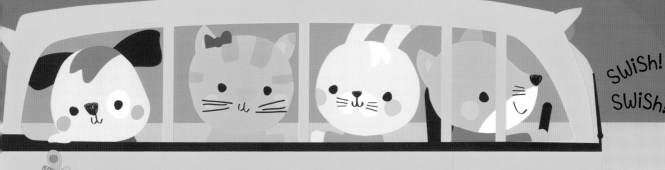

SWiSH!
SWiSH!

Head, Shoulders, Knees and toes

Head, shoulders, knees and toes; knees and toes.
Head, shoulders, knees and toes; knees and toes.
And eyes and ears and mouth and nose.
Head, shoulders, knees and toes; knees and toes.

POllY, PUt the kettle on

Polly, put the kettle on.
Polly, put the kettle on.
Polly, put the kettle on.
We'll all have tea.

Sukey, take it off again.
Sukey, take it off again.
Sukey, take it off again.
They've all gone away.

mary had a little lamb

Mary had a little lamb,
little lamb, little lamb.
Mary had a little lamb.
Its fleece was white as snow.

If you're happy and you know it

If you're happy and you know it,
clap your hands.
If you're happy and you know it,
clap your hands.
If you're happy and you know it,
and you really want to show it,
if you're happy and you know it,
clap your hands.

Rock-a-bye baby

Rock-a-bye baby
on the treetop.
When the wind blows,
the cradle will rock.
When the bough breaks,
the cradle will fall
and down will come baby,
cradle and all.

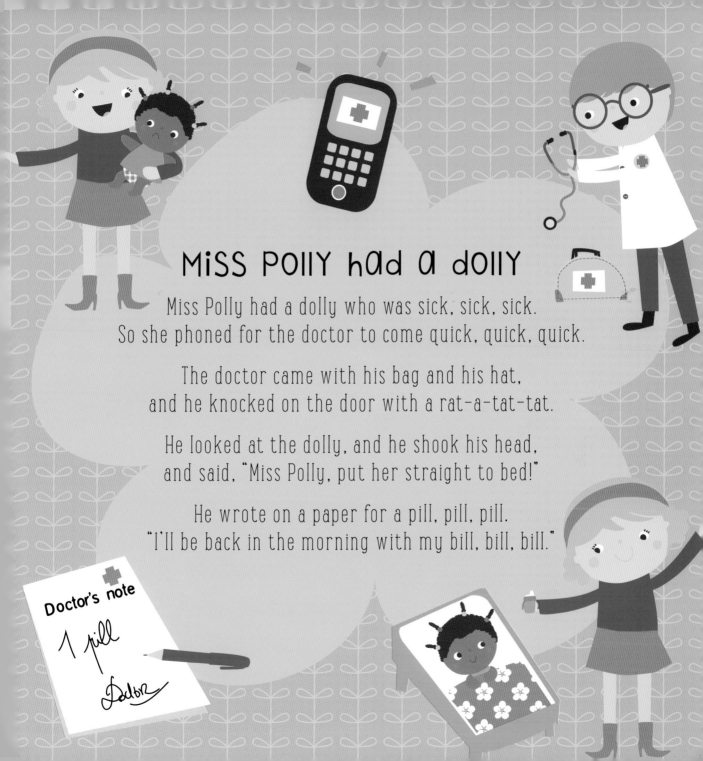

MiSS POllY had a dollY

Miss Polly had a dolly who was sick, sick, sick.
So she phoned for the doctor to come quick, quick, quick.

The doctor came with his bag and his hat,
and he knocked on the door with a rat-a-tat-tat.

He looked at the dolly, and he shook his head,
and said, "Miss Polly, put her straight to bed!"

He wrote on a paper for a pill, pill, pill.
"I'll be back in the morning with my bill, bill, bill."

Doctor's note

1 pill

Old MacDonald

Old MacDonald had a farm,
E-I-E-I-O.
And on his farm he had a cow,
E-I-E-I-O.
With a moo, moo here,
and a moo, moo there.
Here a moo,
there a moo,
everywhere a moo, moo.
Old MacDonald had a farm,
E-I-E-I-O.

Three blind mice

Three blind mice!
Three blind mice!
See how they run!
See how they run!
They all ran after the farmer's wife,
who cut off their tails with a carving knife.
Did you ever see such a thing in your life
as three blind mice?

TOWN

yankee Doodle

Yankee Doodle went to town,
riding on a pony.
Stuck a feather in his hat
and called it macaroni!

I'm a little teapot

I'm a little teapot,
short and stout.
Here's my handle;
here's my spout.
When I get all steamed up,
hear me shout!
Tip me over,
and pour me out!

Little Bo Peep

Little Bo Peep has lost her sheep
and doesn't know where to find them.
Leave them alone, and they'll come home,
wagging their tails behind them.

Sing a song of sixpence

Sing a song of sixpence,
a pocket full of rye,
four and twenty blackbirds
baked in a pie.
When the pie was opened,
the birds began to sing.
Oh, wasn't that a dainty dish
to set before the king?

The king was in his counting house,
counting out his money;
the queen was in the parlour,
eating bread and honey;
the maid was in the garden,
hanging out the clothes,
when down came a blackbird
and pecked off her nose.